D1453994

# Strength of a Lion,

## *Soul of a Lamb*

## A Collection of Wolfhound Fairy Tales and Poetry

# Shirl Knobloch

* * *

*Strength of a Lion, Soul of a Lamb: A Collection of Wolfhound Fairy Tales and Poetry*

© Shirley Knobloch, 2016

Edited by:  Jennifer Sabatelli

Cover Artwork by:  Shirl Knobloch

Photography by:  Shirl Knobloch

ISBN 13:  978-0-9974752-0-3

Also by Shirl Knobloch:

✍ *Birdsong, Barks, and Banter:  Adventures of an Animal Intuitive Reiki Master and Her Home of Misfit Companions*

✍ *The Returning Ones:  A Medium's Memoirs*

✍ *You're Never Too Old for Fairy Tales*

✍ *Reenactments from My Heart:  Spiritual and Supernatural Civil War Fiction and Poetry*

✍ *Once Upon a Fairy Tale*

• • •

*Dedicated to Oscar, the first Irish Wolfhound to walk at my side in the Irish rain. May he now roam beautiful green fields, in spirit.*

*And to my own Aura Lea*

. . .

# Table of Contents

* * *

. . .

# Prologue

I have always wanted a Wolfhound. Perhaps there is an ancient memory in my soul of distant centuries and long gone companions once by my side.

The longing intensified when I visited Ireland and met a gentle Irish Wolfhound named Oscar who lived at Cabra Castle. Oscar died a couple of years later. I dedicate this book to him and to my own Wolfhound, Aura Lea. They truly are gentle giants, huge in body and in heart.

# To Never Break One's Heart

Once upon a time, in a land of rough seas, jagged cliffs, and green forests, there lived a chieftain. A powerful man, he ruled over many clans and held dominion over all who inhabited his territory.

As many of his time, fear of the unknown mysteries and powers terrified him. What he could not fight with a sword and shield had to be eliminated from his realm by any means possible. He ordered his clansmen to remove all the gypsies from the forests, to destroy all camps, and to kill all who refused to flee his lands. Many were killed—women, children, as well as fathers who fought to save what little possessions they owned.

One gypsy woman slipped into the chieftain's castle. She had lost everything; she had watched her husband and brothers die. All that filled her heart was revenge. She poisoned the chieftain and his wife and sought to seek vengeance on all he loved.

But her gypsy heart waivered at the sight of a small toddler playing by his crib. She could not kill him, for he was an innocent, just like those she loved who had been slain. Instead, she turned him into another being. A massive creature with long legs, swift in flight, with large teeth able to tear flesh apart, and with fur the color of early morning mist. She sealed the curse with the words, *"Until you break another's heart."*

And so, the being roamed the forests. His towering size concealed an even more massive heart. For he was a gentle being, with kind brown eyes that felt the sorrow and pain of all the creatures of the forest in which he roamed. He could not hurt another living being. He refused to hunt and foraged along with the antlered beings he called friends. His massive paws never hurt those that walked the forest beside him, from the tiniest birds to the powerful wolves that howled in the night. He kept hidden in the shadows, for he could not bear the fear on human faces as they gazed upon his size.

He had no memory of his past; the gypsy's curse had eradicated all traces of his humanity. He knew nothing of his heritage, of the lands and castles owned, of the cruelty set upon the land by his own father. Although his friends were all the creatures of the forest, his lonely heart longed for more, but he could not understand just what that more might be. He wandered the heather and moss-laden fields, he marveled at the standing stones under the quiet of the moonlight, and he spent several years with only the hares and foxes and wolves and deer as his companions.

In another part of the land lived a kind king and queen. They had a daughter with beauty as shimmering as the wild sea. Her name was Rose. Rose would have been the prize of any chieftain or king throughout the country, but she could not walk. She spent her days in loneliness, her only companions being the nurse and the servants her father hired. Rose was dearly loved by her parents. Her father feared his daughter would never truly be loved, that she would solely be wooed for the dowry she brought to a husband. The castles, the lands, the armies—that was why a man would want her, not for the sweet soul she truly was.

The king created a lovely garden for Rose. Within it, heather, daffodils, wisteria, lilies, orchids, and daisies bloomed. Rose would sit there in the morning sun, watching the world go by. One morning, a large, grey dog appeared out of the woods. Rose was not like the others; she did not fear him. He crept closer. He heard one of Rose's ladies in waiting scream. "No, he is no danger," cried Rose. She held out her hand, and the wild creature nuzzled his shaggy head under it.

Rose gazed into his enormous brown eyes. She felt the sorrow and loneliness and told him he would never be alone again. And he wasn't. She called him Mo Chara, my friend. Her father said he was a Wolfhound, a hunter of beasts. But

Chara possessed a gentle heart, with not a mean bone in his powerful body.

And a truer friend there never was. Chara was always at her side, from the moment she awakened her kind, blue eyes to the moment she closed their heavy lids in slumber. The nurse protested, saying such a beast was unclean and should not be permitted in Rose's bed chamber, but Rose's pleas to her father prevailed.

Years passed. Rose told all her secrets to Chara. He listened to every one. She told him of dreams of princes and knights and wishes for love and happiness. But Chara also listened to the sad conversations of a king and queen and how those wishes would never be fulfilled.

Many years went by, and Rose's loveliness increased with each day. But alas, her legs were still withered and useless. Her life was doomed to be a lonely one, except for Chara. One night, Chara made up his mind to venture off to find a prince or knight for Rose. He gazed at her sleeping face and kissed her with his sizeable snout. Rose awakened and seemed to know that Chara had to leave. "Return to me," she whispered in his ear. Then, she watched him slip away in darkness while all the castle slept.

He roamed for many days and came upon another castle. A powerful chieftain lived there. He saw Chara and tied a lead around his neck. "You will make a fine hunter," he exclaimed. And so, Chara was led out into the fields where his antlered friends and the wolves lived. Chara refused to hunt. The chieftain beat his back until bloody, and Chara was left out in the woods alone. But he wasn't alone; the forest beings remembered him. They brought him nourishment and nursed him back to health.

On he went, this time coming upon a massive fortress filled with knights. "Oh, what an asset to have in our battle," a knight exclaimed. So they tied a lead around his neck and led him into a place of terror, bloodshed, and killing. Chara refused to fight. The knights abandoned him in the woods.

By now, Chara was very tired and realized how true the king and queen's words were. He must go home to Rose and keep her heart from being lonely. If no prince or knight would love her, he would spend the rest of his life doing so.

Many days of journey lay before Chara. He wasn't as young as the mass of fur that once came out of the woodlands to a princess's garden. But love gave him strength.

Rose spied him from the garden. She held out her arms and grasped his shaggy fur. "Oh, my Chara, how I have missed you!" she cried. "I knew you would return to me." Chara's eyes looked into hers with more love than he had ever known before. But he was tired; the journey had taken away much strength. His sore paws felt the pain of every rock on the path, his long legs ached, and he felt it hard to stand. With just enough strength, he walked beside as servants carried Rose back to her chamber.

Rose was snuggled into bed with Chara by her bedside. He draped his head into the crook of her elbow and looked sorrowfully into her eyes. *Goodbye my sweetest Rose*, he thought, for he knew he was dying. His breaths were labored, his vision diminished. He could only feel the warmth of her tear-stained face as she held his face close to her own. And then his breathing stopped.

"No! Mo Chara!" she cried. "Do not leave me!" She felt her heart break in two within. And then she saw the light. A beautiful light surrounded Chara's still body. The curse had been broken, for Chara had caused another heart to break, something impossible for his living body to do. Only in death had he accomplished this feat. True to her word, the gypsy's curse was lifted.

* * *
9

Now, the young man remembered who he was, who his father had been. He went to the king and offered his castle and lands for the hand of the beautiful Rose. And together, the two lived the rest of their lives in happiness and peace. All were welcomed in their kingdom. No creatures were looked upon in fear, and no humans brought terror from misunderstanding again. And always, Wolfhounds roamed the castle grounds.

# The Path of
# Goodness

Once upon a time, in a rugged burren landscape, there lived a wise old crone and her Wolfhound, Maugrim. The crone was a healer, by day collecting herbs and blossoms to make her tinctures and teas, and by night mixing oils and balms for salves and ointments. Together, she and Maugrim walked the barren paths and backwoods, seeking to help those in need. More than a dozen babies owed their lives to the midwifery skills of the crone. Together, she and her Wolfhound stopped and prayed at the stone cairns and burial mounds, leaving wildflowers as tokens of respect.

Not all heeded the pair with kindness. Some muttered *witch* under their breaths as she passed by, walking stick on one side and Maugrim on the other. But the pair was inseparable, that is, until the day they came. She felt them coming. She knew that her simple life with Maugrim was over.

She tossed her oils and balms on the fire one by one. She crumbled her dried herbs into dust. She left nothing behind, nothing for them to look upon. She laid a wrinkled hand on Maugrim's chest. "Be well, my dear friend. Always remember to treat others with kindness." As she lifted her hand away, the patch of fur on Maugrim's grey chest turned to a heart-shaped fluff of white. "Keep a heart filled with the white light of kindness, Maugrim," she whispered.  Maugrim held out his paw.  She grasped its tip, and it too turned to white.

"Walk the path of goodness, Maugrim," she whispered.

To this day, all descendants of Maugrim have a heart-shaped patch of white fur on their chests and four white-tipped paws. Wildflowers dot the burren on the spot where a humble cottage once stood, a cottage filled with kindness and light that lives on in the hearts of Wolfhounds everywhere.

# Wolfhound Eyes

Eyes to hunt a wolf

Take down a human heart

In seconds


A heart is lost

Given without fight

To eyes that wield

More power

Than a sword


Eyes that see

What others miss

Through years of knowing

Seen in seconds

The colors of one's soul


Eyes that feel

What has been hidden

Lifetimes

Absorbed in

Minutes


Eyes that link

Two other eyes

Not for a lifetime

But for eternity


Time has no meaning

All that was

Sees again

Exists again

Through Wolfhound

Eyes

# Every Stitch in Place

aeve and Marjorie were two Wolfhound sisters who lived by the Irish sea with their mom, Marina. They loved little more than romping along the rocky beach, playing with pieces of driftwood and dipping their paws into the chilly waves.

Marina was an artist. She could create beauty out of any debris washed ashore. Shells were intricately woven into wind chimes that sang at her door. Pieces of driftwood became scenes of the Irish landscape. Fishermen came to Marina to repair the holes in nets. Marina could get each stitch perfectly in place like no other in her village.

One day, Maeve and Marjorie were playing tug of war on the beach. Marina looked out her window and saw them clutching something dark and shiny in the sun. Marina's heart fluttered. She yelled out the window for them to drop it and raced down to the beach to retrieve their toy.

It was a seal pelt, shiny in the afternoon sun. The Wolfhounds had torn several holes in it and were not too eager to give up their find. After a bit of scolding, they moved on to a piece of driftwood. Marina gingerly picked up the pelt in her arms. How wonderful it felt! How soft and soothing, how right in her arms. She carried it home and worked through the night repairing each tear, placing each stitch in just the right place. Marina knew the contours of this shape, knew just how tight to stretch the skin, knew just how close together to sew the stitches for the perfect repair. As she draped it across her arms, how inviting it felt! How lovely to just place it across her shoulders.

But in that moment, Maeve and Marjorie looked up at Marina with their large, loving eyes. *Who would care for them*, Marina wondered. *No, it is not mine.* She finished the last stitch and placed it in her basket high up in the closet, out of harm's reach.

The next morning, Marina walked down to the rocks and laid the pelt on top. She climbed the path back home and crouched behind a tall hedge, watching. Soon, a beautiful maiden approached the rocks. She took hold of the pelt, and for one brief moment, she seemed to look in Marina's direction and smile. Then, she disappeared into the sea. How Marina wished someone had found what she had lost so many years ago. Perhaps they had and hid it. Perhaps it still lay among the crevices of the rocky beach.

But a familiar sound distracted her attention. Marina heard the barking of Maeve and Marjorie and walked through her doorway as the seashells chimed above her head. One day, when her mortal body was turned into ash and tossed into the sea, she would become a seal again.

*(I based this fairy tale on the Selkie legends of Ireland. A Selkie is thought to shed his or her seal pelt and take on human form. They may return to the sea only if they find their pelts again.)*

# A Wolfhound in the House

If you've ever had your body

Whipped by a Wolfhound tail

If your small place on the sofa

Has you curled up like a snail


If you've ever had the paw prints

Of a Wolfhound in the rain

Leave a muddy trail behind

On floors and cushions stained


If you've ever had a wet mouth

Drip pools across the floor

And then set upon your lap

Now drenching to the core


If you've had a Wolfhound snout

Come closely in your space

As you took a bite of sandwich

Or placed a cookie to your face


If you've ever had a pair

Of soulful, loving eyes

Gaze upon you in your sadness

Well, then you've realized


That the paw prints, drool, and puddles

Are pittance price to pay

When a Wolfhound comes to share

Your home and heart this way.

# Wolfhound Heaven

There is a special Angel

Soft wings of sparkling dew

Who greets each Wolfhound spirit

When their time on earth is through


Such gentle, loving beings

Have a special place reserved

Among the fields of Heaven

A place so much deserved


Soft pastures, mossy green,

And lavender so fair

The scent of roses blooming

Pervades the fragrant air


With snouts raised high

In wonder

The Wolfhounds greet the sun

In Heaven with the Angels

Their place so rightly won


They wait there in the

Gardens

They run among the glens

Until the day the Angels

Bring loved ones home again


Each time a Wolfhound crosses

An Angel sheds a tear

For every human heart

Now left with grief to bear


A heart filled up with sorrow

A home too free of space

An emptiness so hollow

That nothing can replace


When years pass far too quickly

And time on earth is through

A Wolfhound's wings are waiting

Soft white, with sparkling dew

# Kind Frederick

*F*rederick was a kind Wolfhound. He lived with his family, Baker Schussler and his wife. Of course, being a baker, Herr Schussler had many tempting treats in his shop. Not just Wolfhounds were tempted—a family of mice called the bakeshop home. Herr Schussler hoped Frederick would solve that problem, but Frederick wouldn't hurt a fly. He became friends with Mother Mouse, bringing her crumbs of pastry when the baker wasn't paying attention, too busy putting loaves into the oven. Frederick got a big bowl of milk in the morning. His shaggy, wet beard dripped puddles along the floor, more than enough for Mother Mouse. She had ten little babies to feed.

One morning, Frederick found Mother Mouse lying very still. Nearby was Herr Schussler's broom. Frederick's eyes filled with tears as he gently picked up his friend and brought her outside in a corner of the garden. He picked up leaves, covered her little body, and put a fallen rose over her grave.

Then he remembered. Her babies! Frederick raced to the corner of the bakery where Mother Mice had made her nest. He found ten little mouths, open and squeaking. Frederick picked up each one gently by its neck and lifted it up over his shoulder. "Climb into my fur and hide!" he whispered. Each mouse snuggled into Frederick's shaggy coat and disappeared.

"Keep hidden," whispered Frederick. "Only come out when I tell you it is safe."

Frederick stole into the bakery kitchen and grabbed a linzer tart, then another, and another. Before Herr Schussler could catch him, he dashed outside into the baker's garden. He lay down close to the ground and told the little babies to climb down slowly, holding onto his fur like a rope. Their hungry mouths made little crumbs of the delicious tarts. Then, they all climbed aboard Frederick and fell asleep.

This continued for days, the babies growing bigger and stronger. It was harder to hide in Frederick's fur, but they all knew what would happen if the baker saw. One morning, Frederick crept into the kitchen and found the baker's wife spreading jam on a piece of stollen. Frederick saw her eyes grow wide as saucers as she looked at him. Ten little heads had popped out on top of Frederick's fur!

The baker's wife was a gentle woman, much kinder than Herr Schussler. She placed a saucer of cream and ten little squares of stollen on the floor for the babies. Then, she placed a bowl of cream and one large slice for Frederick. "I will keep your secret, little ones," she whispered. "Now hurry, run and hide before my husband returns from his deliveries."

Each night, Frederick carried his family to the village fountain. One by one, they slid down his fur and bathed in the water. One by one, they climbed on top their Wolfhound dad and nestled back inside his warm, comforting coat.

The day comes when all parents must bid farewell to their children and send them on their own way. That sad day came too soon for Frederick. How he would miss them! Before they left, Frederick carried them all to the corner of the garden where a little mouse lay. Each baby mouse left a tiny petal on her grave and said goodbye. Because of a kind-hearted Wolfhound, they all had new lives to begin.

As for Frederick, his heart was soothed by a big piece of gingerbread the baker's wife had waiting in her kitchen. "You're a good boy, Frederick," she whispered as she kissed the top of his head.

# The Irish Rose

aeve was a new widow, still crying over the loss of her husband of fifty years. She shared her cottage with Liam, her faithful hound.

Each day of their marriage, Maeve's husband would bring her a wild rose, the ones that bloomed in the woodlands at the edge of their land. Maeve would awaken and find one on her bedside pillow or on the farmhouse table. Maeve woke the morning after Connor's death to find no rose, just an empty place at her bedside.

Maeve spent the past week crying, with the empathic eyes of Liam gazing up at her. Liam was Connor's constant companion, roaming the Irish woodlands each day. What Connor did, Liam witnessed. Now, Liam knew what must be done.

He went to the woodlands and chewed through a wild rose stem. This took an enormous act of love, since thorns grew with the roses. Maeve was out back hanging clothes while Liam crept back inside the farmhouse. Gently, he placed the rose on the kitchen table.

Maeve came back inside and burst into tears. Then, she saw the tiny drops of blood on Liam's beard and knew. A caring hound had brought an Irish rose of love.

# The Christmas Mosquito

ossy was a little mosquito who lived with her mama and papa in an old library.  Among the dusty shelves, Mossy would buzz, entranced by all the pictures of a world she had never seen.

The library was home.  During the warm months of the year, Mossy and her parents would live among the books, coming out only to take a drink from one of the library felines who slept on large cushions on the floor.  During the colder months, Mossy and her parents went to sleep in a tiny crack in the floorboard under the librarian's front desk.

Of all the books, Mossy loved the Christmas pictures.  The beautiful glitter on the Christmas trees, the pictures of Santa and his reindeer, and all the sparkling pages of lights and decorations captivated the kind little mosquito's heart.

The librarian had a gentle Wolfhound named William.  William slept by her side, greeted library guests with a wagging tail, and gave sloppy kisses to all who patted his large head.

"Is he a reindeer, mama?"  Mossy asked.

"No, Mossy, he is the librarian's wolfhound."

"He is big enough to be a reindeer," Mossy cried. To her eyes, William surely was a giant, strong enough to pull Santa's sleigh. "Why can't we stay for Christmas, mama?" she mournfully asked. Oh, to see the trees and the lights just one Christmas Day! How this little mosquito longed in her heart for this wish.

"We cannot stay for Christmas, Mossy. It will be too cold. We have to be snuggled in our beds until the days become warm again."

Summer days dwindled into autumn chills, and mama and papa began preparing their nests. Mossy spent hours gazing at the picture books, still longing to see her first Christmas.

"Come Mossy, we must hide," cried mama.

"No, mama," answered Mossy. "I am not going to sleep. I am staying for Christmas."

Mama begged her little daughter to come sleep, but Mossy refused. With a tearful eye, mama kissed her tiny daughter's head. "I love you, Mossy. May you be safe until the spring." With that, mama piled a bit of dust in front of the floorboard crack for insulation and waved farewell.

Days were getting chillier, and nights were becoming colder. Mossy took just enough to drink from the library cats to survive, for she was a kind and gentle soul. "Christmas must be soon," she whispered to herself.

Then one day, the librarian put a pair of reindeer antlers on William's head. "I knew you were a reindeer!" Mossy shrieked. "You can take me to Christmas!" Mossy climbed on top of William's head. She nestled in among his long, shaggy fur and waited until the library closed.

Then, she was outside! William raced across the snow. The lights of the village sparkled just like in the library picture books. Mossy saw red and blue and green shimmering on the trees. "How beautiful!!!" she cried. "Oh, mama, I wish you could see Christmas!"

It was very, very cold. William's fur kept Mossy safe. But everything was just too beautiful. They passed a large tree, aglow in brilliant white lights, with a shining star nestled on top. "Oh," sighed Mossy. "Christmas is lovelier than any picture book!" With that, she flew up into the wind and landed on a high branch. She was so tired; her tiny wings were too cold to fly off to find her furry reindeer friend.

Mossy closed her tiny eyes. "Mama, I have found Christmas," she whispered. Then, she closed her weary eyes and spent eternity in a place of unending light.

# The Maiden, the Wolfhound, and the Magic Cap

nce upon a time, there lived a beautiful maiden named Aura. Her humble cottage housed little possessions. Her two heart treasures were a beautiful cap, knitted by her grandmother, and her loyal Wolfhound, William.

Aura's grandmother had died several years before. Aura's only keepsake of her was this cap, and she loved it dearly. William was her grandmother's Wolfhound. Aura promised to keep William safe at Grandma's dying bedside, and she kept that promise for many years. She dearly loved William; he was her constant companion. Not a day went by that those in the village did not see Aura and her colorful cap, William at her side, walking through the woods.

Aura's cap was knitted in layer after layer of beautiful scraps of yarn, each layer held together by tiny pearl buttons. A colorful band of yarn formed the base of the cap, and arranged in rows were layer after layer of colorful stripes. There was a red stripe, a blue stripe, a green stripe. At the very top was one fluffy white pom-pom that seemed to dance with each of Aura's steps. It wasn't hard to spot Aura and William in the woods surrounding town. Other villagers couldn't miss the dancing stripes and pom-pom and the galloping Wolfhound by her side as they ran and played together each day.

Aura had little, but what she possessed was happily shared. Times grew very hard; food was scarce and the winter seemed much harsher than usual. Aura wasn't worried, though. She remembered her grandmother's last words to her: *As long as you have your cap, you will be safe.*

"Is it a magic cap, Grandma?" Aura asked.

"Yes, quite magical, my child. It is filled with love and happiness."

Each day, Aura and William walked the woods, looking for any edible herbs and mushrooms that might have survived the season. Each day, they passed others in the village searching for the same. Aura would share all she collected, but soon there was none left to share.

One day, Aura and William passed a young mother holding a tiny infant in her arms. "Please child, do you have any food? My baby is starving," she cried.

Aura didn't have anything. She owned nothing, nothing except for her magic cap. Aura took the cap off her head. She undid the first row of pearl buttons and handed the red stripe of knitted yarn to the mother. "Take this home and you will be safe." The mother put the stripe of red inside her coat pocket and returned home, not fully understanding or believing the girl's words. Aura placed the cap back on her head and went home.

When Aura reached her tiny cottage, there was a beautiful bushel of red apples on her table waiting. "Thank you, Grandma," she whispered. And she and William filled their tummies with the juicy apples.

When the young mother reached home, she placed her hand inside her coat pocket and found an apple where the knitted stripe had been. She cut into it and found a sparkling ruby! Oh, what this beautiful gem could buy! Her baby would be safe. "Thank you, Aura," she cried.

The next day, Aura met an old gentleman leaning on a walking stick to balance his hunched frame. "Do you have any food?" he asked. "I am old and homeless, and the nights are too cold on my tired bones. Please help me."

Aura didn't have any food. She and William had finished all the apples that morning. But Aura undid the buttons on Grandma's cap and handed the blue stripe to the old man. "Thank you, child, this stripe will keep my neck warm." Aura smiled, hoping it would do much more. And so it did. Aura went home to find a basket of ripe, sweet blueberries on her table. William's beard was blue with delight as they shared this treasure together.

That night, the old man wrapped the scarf around his neck and felt warmer than he had felt in many, many nights. In the morning, he unraveled it and found a large, blue sapphire within the folds of yarn. "Thank you, kind child," the old man cried, for now he would be safe.

The next day Aura and William once again went in search of food, their blueberries all finished. Soon, the pair came upon an old crone in the woods, her basket for collecting herbs empty. "Can you spare a crumb of bread, my child?" the old woman whispered in a weak voice. "I have not eaten in days, and my aging eyes cannot find any food among the dried leaves of the woods. Please help me."

Aura undid the pearl buttons and handed her a green stripe. "Believe in magic, for this is a magic cap," she told the old crone. The crone placed the stripe of yarn in her basket and headed home. With each step, her basket seemed to grow heavier. She looked down and saw it filled with green, leafy vegetables. "Thank you, little child," she cried. Now she was safe.

Aura and William went home, as well. On their table, a bunch of fresh greens waited. Aura made them into a delicious soup and filled two bowls, one for her and one for William.

The next day, Aura and William came upon a crying little boy. "Can you please help me? I am lost and hungry and cold. I do not know my way home," he sobbed. Aura knew she had only one more stripe left. She undid the last row of buttons and handed the little boy the purple stripe. "This is a magic yarn," she told the boy. "It will help you find home again."

Then Aura and William returned home. Aura's heart was happy, knowing her grandmother's magic would indeed lead the little boy home. "He will be safe," she sighed. No food was waiting at their tiny cottage, though. "Maybe Grandma's magic has worn out," she told William. "All I have left is the band of yarn scraps and the fluffy pom-pom."

She took the band of scraps from Grandma's cap and placed it on William's neck. "You are such a loyal friend," she sobbed. "This will make you a handsome collar. I wish I could give you more." Aura placed the tiny pom-pom in her hand and clutched it tightly. "This is all I have left of you, Grandma," she cried.

Aura's hand grew very hot. The pom-pom shone into a sparkly ball of light. It grew so bright that Aura could not see. When it dimmed, she saw a handsome prince standing where William had been. The Prince held the colored band of yarn in his hands.

"I will keep you safe forever, Aura," he whispered.

# Leaf Charmers

Within each tree lives a charmer

A siren of the woods


From the first flight of a wooden swing

Under her grasp


From the first climb up a sturdy tree house

Sheltered by her leaves


We are entranced


We are lulled to sleep by the swoosh of her arms

In the cold of winter's night

We are smitten by her artist canvas

When Autumn brings her sight


To our charmed eyes


Yes, within each tree lives a charmer

A mermaid of the woods


Singing, calling for us to listen

Some of us do

And our love is life long

From our first glimpse

To the day we close our eyes

And wish to rest beneath

With a loyal Wolfhound placed

By our side

For eternity

# Reflection and Shadow

I think I should like to be a tall tree

Looming over a brook or stream

Watching my reflection in the sunlight

Gazing at my shadow in the moonlight

Oh, what secrets I have kept

Only those who speak to me

Will learn a tiny piece of my soul

Only those who run their fingers over my trunk

One ring on a map of hundreds

One hour in the sunlight

One shadowed evening under the moon

Oh, what secrets I have kept.............

# The Woods

He remembers

Legs twitching

Distant yelps

Paw nails clicking on the wooden floor


He dreams of the woods

Moss and crinkled leaves underfoot

The smell of last night's rain


And the man

His tweed cap shielding the morning mist

His walking stick guiding their path


Was it a dream?

No, it was home.


Then the man could no longer walk

Then his bedroom became the forest

He had to traverse each day

Barely making it to the bathroom

And back

He sat by his bed

Watching, waiting for the man

To get up and put on his tweed cap

And reach for his walking stick


Look, he would plead with his large brown eyes

The rain has stopped

Listen, he would bark and toss his shaggy ears

The linnets are singing


But the man could not raise his head

Or rise from bed.


The end came peacefully.

And the dog was leashed

And journeyed to the home

Of his master's daughter


It was a kind home

A still home

The daughter worked and left

Him alone

To dream


On polished wood floors

Where no moss or leaves

Invaded


He no longer ran in the woods,

Only in dreams

Like today

Was it a dream?

No, it was real.

Look, he could see the old man raising his cap

Listen, he could hear him whisper


Remember me, my friend

I am waiting

In such glorious woods


Look, can you see the mist?

Listen, can you hear the linnets?

# The Wolfhound and the Dove

Each day he sat under the oak

His old bones soothed by the soft grass


Too tired for the chase

Let the hares run free

Let the squirrels be unafraid

For they have not to fear


For he was an old and gentle king

His hunting days had ended

Now just a patch of grass

Beneath an oak and dove

Was all he sought


Each day she cooed and sang

Above his head

A peaceful lullaby

Soothing him to sleep


The once mighty king of his domain

When oak leaves crowned his head

And soft grass formed his throne

And one faithful subject

The musician of his Royal Court

Trumpeted

His presence

To all who walk these fields

Bow your head to his Majesty

For once a King's legs

Flew swiftly as a dove's wings

Where an old and tired soul

Lies in repose

The grass that soothed his bones

Now grows above him

A cairn of stone

Marks the place

Where a Wolfhound

Watched his final sunset

With dove song

In this hallowed place

Now hares nest in the soft grass

And squirrels climb the towering oak

And beneath both

A gentle king slumbers

In eternal peace

Soothed by the sound of a dove.

# Soul Friend

aoilainn was a frail child, with hair the color of a raven's wing and eyes that shone the blue of Ireland skies. Though she was a quiet child, her head soaked up stories of fairies and leprechauns like a sponge. Her imagination was as wild as the Irish sea. She was the only child of Moira and Ciaran Connor; they adored her.

Not frail in spirit, Caoilainn possessed a fiery spirit. She insisted on walking the woodland path to school and back each day. Moira knew the precise amount of time it took her daughter to make the journey. She positioned herself at the cottage door and waited for her little one to appear.

One afternoon, Caoilainn was late. Ten minutes late. Ten heart-wrenching moments for Moira. Then her daughter appeared. "I am all right, mama. I had to walk slowly because my friend has a limp, and his steps are not as quick as mine."

"Your friend?" Caoilainn's mother asked. She knew all the village children and not one took this path home.

"See him, mama? Isn't he beautiful?"

Caoilainn pointed to the edge of the woodland path. Moira searched the horizon but saw no one. "There!" shouted Caoilainn. But still, her mother saw no one.

"He is so soft and warm. He lets me put my arms around him and hold him tight."

By now, Caoilainn's mother was quite frantic. "Who is this friend?"

"He is my Wolfhound. Can't you see him, mama? I call him Anam. I love him, mama. He is my best friend!"

Moira took Caoilainn by the hand and took her inside the cottage. "Oh, my little one's imagination," she whispered to herself.

"Mama, can we leave a dish outside for Anam. He must be so hungry, and his sore leg must hurt him so. Please, mama?" Food was scarce enough without feeding an imaginary dog, but Moira talked it over with Caoilainn's dad that night. They decided there was no harm in leaving one tiny bowl of stew out, so the little girl placed it at the edge of the path and whispered in the woods for her friend to come eat.

This went on for days. Caoilainn's parents began to worry more about their precious daughter's loneliness and need to imagine a furry friend.

Each day, she walked home from school a bit late with the same excuse. Anam's limp took longer to stride the path. Each night, she begged and even left a bit of her own meal to add to Anam's bowl. The bowl was always empty in the morning, but with all the woodland creatures, no wonder its contents were gone. But it was indeed strange that the bowl was never dragged off, just neatly left in the exact spot Caoilainn had placed it the night before.

Moira had much work to do. It was autumn, and the field's harvest must be tended to and the gardens prepared for next spring's planting. When Caoilainn was at school, she harvested the potatoes and cleared all the dry twigs and branches from the summer season.

Then, she spied a large bone among the debris. It looked like a large dog bone, a leg bone. "How strange," she whispered to herself. Moira had been taught to respect all the energies of nature and gently buried the bone in a corner of her garden. She said a little prayer of peace for whoever had once called this place home.

That afternoon, Caoilainn was late, very late. Moira began to worry. She stood at her cottage door, eyes pierced on the path. Then she saw him. A beautiful grey dog, a Wolfhound. He stared right into her eyes and beckoned her to the path. Moira followed. She ran. He ran faster. She lost sight of him. Then she heard her daughter's quiet cries. "Anam! Anam! Please help me!"

Caoilainn had fallen and hit her head on a jagged stone. She was bleeding. Moira scooped her up in her arms and carried her home. She washed her wound and wrapped her in her soothing arms.

"Anam ran away! He never ran before. He ran to help me, mama, I know it. You saw him too, didn't you?"

Moira nodded her head. Who was this dog? A dog that limped and then ran. And did the leg bone belong to him? Was he now whole again? Is that why he lingered on the path, looking for the piece of him to make him run again, to make him be at peace?

Caoilainn looked for Anam each day, but weeks passed. She called and called. Her mother now walked her to school and back home again, her eyes also searching for a glimpse of the large grey being.  But he was gone.

Moira always said a prayer at the corner grave in her garden each day, thanking him for helping her child.  And Christmas brought a special blessing to the pretty cottage, a baby Wolfhound.

"Oh," Caoilainn cried.  "He is so beautiful!  I will call him Anam after my best friend."

Sometimes, in the coldest of winter evenings, Moira carried a tiny bowl out to the edge of the woodland path.  "Here, my friend.  Thank you."

# Drawn Spirit

*F*rancis was at home in the woods. He had no time for books; his teachers were the trees, as were the standing stones, the ancient mounds and fairy forts of the rock-walled fields surrounding his family's cottage. His pockets bulged with all sorts of magickal things, his eyes peering at the ground for a glimpse of a fairy or leprechaun along the path.

One day, he saw him. A large hound, high on the hill, watching over. His massive paws held up a strong, muscular body, covered in shaggy hair the color of Ireland's mist. Francis called to him, but the creature disappeared from sight. Francis liked to draw. He carried a pencil and paper wherever he wandered. He quickly took them out and drew the hound. "I will find you," he whispered. It was nearing sunset, and Francis had to get home. "I will come again tomorrow," he promised.

Tomorrow brought heavy rain. Francis sat sorrowfully at his cottage window, watching the horizon for his hound. "What are you looking at?" his mother questioned. "For him, Ma," Francis answered, showing her his drawing. "My, what a fine beast," his mother replied. "But don't you get too close. You never know what he will do."

Darkness came early that day, and Francis went to bed with the sound of rain pattering against his window. Then he heard it. Was it a bark........no, more like a howl faintly in the distance. Again, he heard it, then no more, as sleep won over his little body.

In the morning, Francis could not eat breakfast fast enough. He hurried out to the fields. "Where are you?" he cried. "I know you are out here. I heard you calling last night." But no creature answered.

Francis followed his usual path, collecting interesting stones, leaves, and pieces of moss along the way. Soon, he came to the same hillside he had visited the day before last. And there he stood. "Come here boy," Francis beckoned. The hound paused, as if to weigh the pros and cons of this gesture. Then, he swiftly ran off beyond the hills.

"I saw him again, Ma!" Francis cried, as he opened the cottage door. "Saw who?" she muttered, busily making dinner. "My hound! He is so beautiful, Ma, like a wild beast of a legend!" he answered. "I told you not to go looking for that creature!!!" Francis mother admonished. "He is no danger, Ma. He is my friend. He called to me last night while I was in my bedroom."

Now, Francis's mother was a bit frightened by those words. Legends and superstitions of wild dogs abound in the county, and not good ones at that. "Francis, I don't want you going out tomorrow." "But Ma!" he cried. "There will be no arguing; that is that. There are plenty of chores around the farm to keep you busy. I won't have you wandering off to meet some wild dog in the woods. Now, hush! Not another word."

Francis slung his head down and went to his room. He took out his pencil and paper and drew more pictures of the hound. He had never drawn so beautifully. The sketches on the paper seemed to come to life. The big, expressive eyes of the creature. His large, black snout. His tall legs and shaggy fur. It was as if his very soul was in the drawing.

Francis minded his ma. He did the chores and stayed close to home for the next few days, all the while thinking of the great hound on the hillside. At night, he sketched and sketched, sometimes stopping to catch a faint howl coming from the edge of the forest.

"You have been such a good boy," Francis mother sighed as her son ate his breakfast oatmeal at the farm table. "Now, we will have no more talk of that hound in this house again."

Francis crumpled his sketches into his trouser pockets, along with his fairy rocks and moss and leaves. He stared at his oatmeal, knowing he must keep his drawings and nighttime howls to himself.

The weather was getting colder. That meant less chores to do about the farm and more days inside by the fire. Francis developed a cough. His ma tried all the home remedies her own ma had taught her, but it worsened each day. At night, she slept by his bedside. Once, she thought she heard howling. *Could it be*, she thought. *No, just a tired mother's imagination, running away with itself.*

Each day, she tried to coax her son to eat. Each day, his strength seemed to weaken. And her strength as well. All the sleepless nights had made her so weary. This night was bitter cold. She bundled Francis in his blankets, but he shivered though sweating. She put her head back to rest in the chair by his side and fell fast asleep.

She awoke with the morning sun. She reached out to feel her son's forehead; it was cold as the winter wind. His eyes were still, his lifeless body still bundled in all his woolen blankets.

Francis was buried behind the cottage. A plain cross marker graced the patch of hard dirt scraped away to create his grave. His mother needed to make it special, but what on this winter's day, with no flowers to honor her son, could she place on his grave?

She thought of his pockets, his treasures. She went into his bedroom and emptied his pockets. There, she found beautiful stones, pieces of green moss, and lovely leaves of green, red, and gold. She wove the moss and leaves into a lovely wreath. She would place the stones around his cross.

And then, she found the crumpled pieces of paper. They were all blank. Not a single picture graced the pages, not a single pencil stroke. *How odd*, she thought. Then, she remembered the drawing her son had shown to her. It was on this very paper. "Now, you are with my son," she cried. She buried her head in her lap, and then she heard it. Just once, a distant howl and the sound of a little boy's laughter. Each night she listened, but she never heard it again. Only once—to say goodbye.

# White Beard

*A*rdan was the son of a powerful chieftain. His father gifted him with his own Wolfhound for his thirteenth birthday. "Now, my son," his father beamed, "you will become a powerful ruler of our clan when your time arises."

Ardan loved the pup. He named him Maugrim, and together, they raced across the heathered fields and forests of his father's land. Maugrim grew into a handsome hound, with a distinctive white beard that graced his chin. The bond between the boy and his white beard was unbreakable. They learned to hunt and be warriors, for a warrior was Ardan's birthright. For two years, they formed one shadow in the Irish sun.

Then one day, Ardan's world was shattered. Enemy clans attacked his father's castle. They killed the chieftain and kidnapped Maugrim. Ardan barely escaped with his life. He spent the next few years plotting his revenge and honing his weaponry skills.

Soon, the day came for Ardan to round up what remained of his clan and take up fight against his enemy. "By the mark of my father's shield, I promise to kill every last one of you." That was the motto by which he lived.

Ardan's skill with the sword and bow were legendary. He had the eyesight of a hawk and an arm stronger than two men. His aim and distance were unparalleled.

Soon, the morning of battle commenced. It was a brilliant day, but no sun could warm the hearts of those filled with hatred. Ardan led his men into the field. Upon the hillside, the enemy clan stood, waiting for the signal to attack. Ardan rallied the clan, his screams filling the air with vengeance. Men fell by the dozens.

Ardan fought with hatred in his eyes, hurling his sword into anything within striking range. Then, he saw the enemy chieftain, his shield shining in the sunlight, glaring Ardan's eyes. Beside him was a large Wolfhound.

Ardan remembered Maugrim, and the hate inside him grew stronger. He surged forward, thrusting his sword into the air. The massive Wolfhound leaped in front of his master, taking the deadly blow. As he fell to the ground, Ardan saw his white beard.

The enemy chieftain fell to the ground and placed his arms around the dying hound. "Kill me, for you have taken my dearest friend," he cried. Tears fell from Ardan's eyes. He dropped his sword and collapsed to the ground beside the chieftain and the gasping dog.  With large eyes, Maugrim looked up at Ardan and lifted his paw. "My dearest friend," he sobbed.

The two chieftains lifted the hound and placed him beneath a cairn of stones. They lay their shields against the cairn and buried their vengeance, as well, that sorrowful day.

# Epilogue

I hope these stories have left readers with a greater understanding of the unique spirits these gentle giants possess. Perhaps that is our compensation for their short lives; their imprint on our hearts is eternal. Sharing a home with one is worth the inevitable heartache that follows too soon.

Endings are never happy, but living with one is always a fairy tale. And that is worth each precious year.

The walk that started it all—Ireland, the rain, and Oscar.

Continuing my wolfhound journey with Aura Lea in Gettysburg.

CPSIA information can be obtained
at www.ICGtesting.com
Printed in the USA
BVHW070206250420
578457BV00004B/1505

9 780997 475203